It's Elementary!

275 Math Word Problems

Book 2

M. J. Owen

Educators Publishing Service, Inc.

Cambridge and Toronto

I dedicate this book to my husband, Will. Thanks for listening to all my classroom stories, teaching methods, and other detailed descriptions and seeing humor in some of it, asking questions about most of it, and supporting me in all of it.

Design by Joyce C. Weston
Illustrations by Tatjana Mai-Wyss

Printed in the U.S.A.
ISBN 0-8388-2412-0

March 2002 Printing

Contents

To the Teacher

Many elementary school students find math word problems to be challenging. In my own classroom, I have found that children often attempt to solve word problems using the wrong operation; for example they may use division instead of multiplication.

The problem-solving approach that I teach my students is called TINS. The letters in this acronym stand for the different steps students use to analyze and solve word problems. While reading a word problem, students circle key words and note their THOUGHT (T) about the operation they should use to solve the problem. Next they circle and write down the important INFORMATION (I) from the word problem. At this stage I also encourage students to draw a picture of the information and to cross out information that doesn't seem important to the problem. Students then write their information as a NUMBER SENTENCE (N) and plug their answer into a SOLUTION SENTENCE (S). Here's an example.

WORK SPACE

Jodi has 6 cats, 4 dogs, and 3 birds. How many dogs and cats does Jodi have in all?

Thought (T): ____+____

Information (I): __6 cats, 4 dogs__

Number Sentence (N): __6 + 4 =__

Solution Sentence (S): __Jodi has 10 cats__ __and dogs.__

I hope this book—which covers addition, subtraction, multiplication, and division—will provide opportunities for fun and success with word problems. Happy problem solving!

Solving Addition Word Problems with TINS

When you are reading a word problem, think of yourself as a super sleuth. Key words can give you clues about how to solve each problem. Here are some addition key words.

 in all   altogether

 sum   total

 add (and added)

You may want to add other addition words you know to this list.

When you see an addition key word in a problem, circle it and write + above the key word. Then write + on the THOUGHT line. Next, circle and write down the important INFORMATION from the word problem. Sometimes it helps to draw a picture of the important information. It's also a good idea to cross out information that doesn't seem important to the problem. Now write your information as a NUMBER SENTENCE. Then plug your answer into your SOLUTION SENTENCE.

Check out this example problem.

Terrell had 7 action figures. His mom took him to the store and let him pick out 4 more. How many action figures does Terrell have now?

Thought: _____ + _____

Information: 7 action figures, 4 action figures

Number Sentence: 7 + 4 =

Solution Sentence: Terrell has 11 action figures.

WORK SPACE

A good way to remember how to solve word problems is to think of the word TINS.

T = Thought
I = Information
N = Number Sentence
S = Solution Sentence

Good luck and happy problem solving!

Try It Out

Use TINS to solve these word problems. Remember to circle key words, draw pictures, and cross out extra information. The first 4 problems have pictures to help you out.

---

1. Marcy went to the store and bought 9 pencils. Her brother bought 6 pencils. How many pencils did Marcy and her brother have altogether?

Thought: _You add them_

Information: _____

_____

Number Sentence: _9+6 = 15_

Solution Sentence: _15 − 6 = 9_

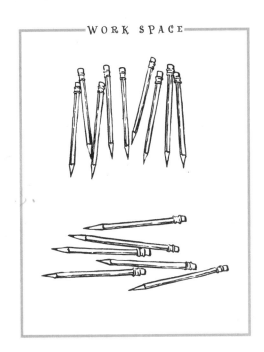

WORK SPACE

---

2. Mrs. Cavazos has 8 thumbtacks. The teacher next door gave her 14 more thumbtacks to hang up her new posters. How many thumbtacks does Mrs. Cavazos have now?

Thought: _You add them_

Information: _____

_____

Number Sentence: _8+14 = 22_

Solution Sentence: _22 − 14 = 8 and_
_22 − 8 = 14_

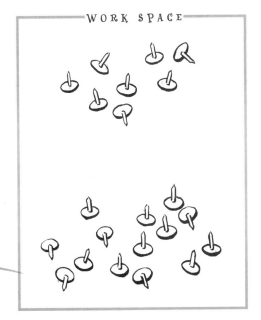

WORK SPACE

ballet school

3. Catheryne invited 4 friends from her class to her birthday party. Later she invited 3 friends from her dance class to the party. How many friends did Catheryne invite in all?

Thought: _you add them_

Information: _____

_____

Number Sentence: _4+3 = 7_

Solution Sentence: _7-3 = 4_

_7-4 = 3_

WORK SPACE

4. Daniel folded several pieces of origami paper and created 9 birds, 7 frogs, 1 star, and 3 mice. How many art pieces did Daniel create?

Thought: _you add them_

Information: _____

_____

Number Sentence: _9+7+1+3 =20_

Solution Sentence: _Too many Numbers!_

WORK SPACE

4 . 32
+ 3 . 46

5. Allison and Andrea went out for breakfast. Allison spent $3.46 and Andrea spent $4.32. How much money did the girls spend in all?

Thought: _you add the money_

Information: _____

Paper _cyrcle_

Number Sentence: _7 + 15 = 22_

Solution Sentence: _22 - 15 = 7_
_22 - 7 = 15_

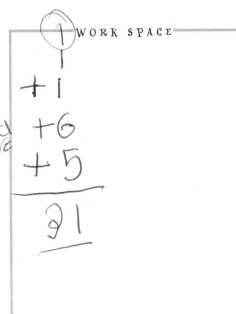

WORK SPACE

78 money   dimes | Pennies

6. Mr. Mazzola's market employs himself, his brother, 6 cousins, and 5 stock boys. How many people work in the market all together?

Thought: _you add himself and brother are each 1 Peaison_

Information: _____

Number Sentence: _1 + 1 + 6 + 5 = 3 1_

Solution Sentence: _8 To many humbers_

WORK SPACE

1
+ 1
+ 6
+ 5
——
2 1

7. The weather forecaster predicts that Philadelphia will receive 15 inches of rain in March, 9 inches of rain in April, 7 inches of rain in May, and 3 inches of rain in June. How much rain is the weather forecaster predicting in total for Philadelphia during March and May?

Thought: _add March +May_

Information: _____

_____

Number Sentence: _15+ 7=22_

Solution Sentence: _____

_____

WORK SPACE

$$\begin{array}{r} 1 \\ 15 \\ +\ 7 \\ \hline 22 \end{array}$$

---

8. The track team at Baty Elementary ran 4 miles on Tuesday, 2 miles on Wednesday, and 3 miles on Thursday. How many miles did the track team run on Tuesday and Thursday?

Thought: _____

Information: _____

_____

Number Sentence: _____

Solution Sentence: _____

_____

WORK SPACE

9. Monique's family went to an amusement park. They spent $78 for the family's entrance fee, $22 on lunch, and $8 on postcards. How much money did Monique's family spend on lunch and postcards while they were in the park?

Thought: _____

Information: _____

_____

Number Sentence: _____

Solution Sentence: _____

_____

WORK SPACE

10. Christian's team hit 3 homeruns on Saturday and 4 homeruns on Sunday. What was the total number of homeruns his team hit on Saturday and Sunday?

Thought: _____

Information: _____

_____

Number Sentence: _____

Solution Sentence: _____

_____

WORK SPACE

Solving Subtraction Word Problems with TINS

You can use TINS to solve subtraction word problems, too! Your assignment: follow the path to find subtraction key words.

- ⊙⟝ left
- ⊙⟝ give (and gave) away
- ⊙⟝ difference

- ⊙⟝ how many more
- ⊙⟝ how much more
- ⊙⟝ subtract

Can you think of any other subtraction key words? If so, add them to the list.

When you see a subtraction key word in a problem, circle it and write – above the key word. Then write – on the THOUGHT line. Next, circle and write down the important INFORMATION from the word problem. Sometimes it helps to draw a picture of the important INFORMATION from the word problem. It's also a good idea to cross out extra information that doesn't seem important to the problem. Now write your information as a NUMBER SENTENCE. Then plug your answer into your SOLUTION SENTENCE.

Example: Lindsey has (18 balloons.) She (gave her friends 11 balloons.) How many balloons does Lindsey have (left?)

Thought: _____ — _____

Information: 18 balloons, gave 11 balloons

_____

Number Sentence: _____ 18 — 11 = _____

Solution Sentence: Lindsey has 7 balloons

_____ left. _____

WORK SPACE

Try It Out

Use TINS to solve these word problems. Remember to circle key words, draw pictures, and cross out extra information. The first 4 problems have pictures to help you.

1. Laverne ate 14 granola bars in May and 18 in June. How many more granola bars did Laverne eat in June?

Thought: _____

Information: _____

_____

Number Sentence: _____

Solution Sentence: _____

_____

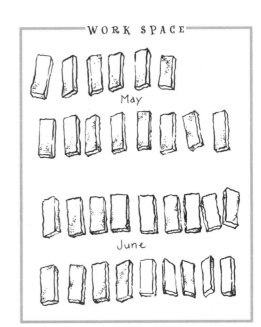

2. Bianca had $42. She spent $28 at the store. How much money does Bianca have now?

T: _____

I: _____

_____

N: _____

S: _____

_____

3. Lucille brought 24 postcards to school. She gave 20 postcards to her classmates. How many postcards did Lucille have left?

T: _____

I: _____

_____

N: _____

S: _____

_____

4. Belle completed 2 hours of homework on Monday, 1 hour on Tuesday, 3 hours on Wednesday, and 2 hours on Thursday. How many more hours of homework did Belle do on Wednesday than on Tuesday?

T: _____

I: _____

_____

N: _____

S: _____

_____

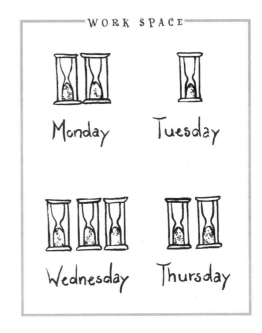

5. Theresa visited the Sears Tower in Chicago and found it was 1,454 feet high. The next month she rode the elevator to the top of the Empire State Building in New York and discovered it was 1,250 feet high. How much higher is the Sears Tower?

T: _____

I: _____

_____

N: _____

S: _____

_____

WORK SPACE

6. A tadpole grew its back legs in 7 weeks. It grew its front legs in 5 weeks. How much longer did it take to grow its back legs?

T: _____

I: _____

_____

N: _____

S: _____

_____

WORK SPACE

7. Miriam saved $78. Mark saved $49. How much more money did Miriam save?

T: _____

I: _____

_____

N: _____

S: _____

_____

WORK SPACE

8. After touring the Biltmore House in North Carolina, Carmen compared the 250 rooms she saw to the 6 rooms in her house. How many more rooms did Carmen find at the Biltmore than in her own house?

T: _____

I: _____

_____

N: _____

S: _____

_____

WORK SPACE

9. Tai is learning the Cambodian language. He notices that the Cambodian alphabet has 72 letters. If the American alphabet has 26 letters, how many more letters are in the Cambodian alphabet?

T: _____

I: _____

_____

N: _____

S: _____

_____

WORK SPACE

---

10. Christopher Columbus sailed from Spain in 1492 on the Santa Maria with a crew of 41 people. In 1620 the Pilgrims set sail on the Mayflower with a total of 102 passengers. How many more people journeyed on the Mayflower than on the Santa Maria?

T: _____

I: _____

_____

N: _____

S: _____

_____

WORK SPACE

Addition and Subtraction Mixed Review: Take the Challenge I

Use TINS to solve the following word problems. Remember to draw pictures, circle key words, and cross out extra information.

1. Charlotte's bookstore had 19 used paperback books in stock. She sold 7 of these books during a sale. How many used paperback books does her bookstore have left?

Thought: _____

Information: _____

_____

Number Sentence: _____

Solution Sentence: _____

_____

WORK SPACE

2. Maude has $56 in her wallet. She spends $33 on new clothes. How much money does Maude have left in her wallet?

T: _____

I: _____

_____

N: _____

S: _____

_____

WORK SPACE

3. The Sherman family drove 188 miles on Monday and 233 miles on Tuesday. How many more miles did the Sherman family drive on Tuesday?

T: _____

I: _____

_____

N: _____

S: _____

_____

WORK SPACE

4. The cafeteria has 21 chairs. Mrs. Willis moves 18 chairs out of the cafeteria for the science fair. How many chairs are left in the cafeteria?

T: _____

I: _____

_____

N: _____

S: _____

_____

WORK SPACE

5. Mr. Chung is selling 125 tickets to the school play. He visited 8 houses on Thursday and 3 houses on Friday. How many houses did Mr. Chung visit in all?

T: _____

I: _____

_____

N: _____

S: _____

_____

WORK SPACE

6. Brenda wrote 7 pages in her new journal on Monday, 5 pages in her journal on Tuesday, and 9 pages in her journal on Friday. What was the total number of pages Brenda wrote in her journal?

T: _____

I: _____

_____

N: _____

S: _____

_____

WORK SPACE

7. Malcolm was assigned 4 pages of math problems. He spent 45 minutes on Saturday and 35 minutes on Sunday. How much time did Malcolm spend studying math over the weekend?

T: _____

I: _____

_____

N: _____

S: _____

_____

WORK SPACE

8. For 22 days in June the temperature in Texas was above 100 degrees. In July, 28 days were also above 100 degrees. How many more 100-degree days were there in July?

T: _____

I: _____

_____

N: _____

S: _____

_____

WORK SPACE

9. Marissa's summer school class travels three days each week. On Monday's field trip they rode 100 miles to the San Antonio zoo. On Wednesday they traveled 33 miles to a state park, and on Friday they journeyed 117 miles to a museum in Houston. How many more miles did Marissa's summer school class drive on Friday than on Wednesday?

T: _____

I: _____

_____

N: _____

S: _____

_____

WORK SPACE

10. Simone had $79. She spent $9 on a new shirt, $11 on a new CD, and $4 on lunch at the mall with Isabella. What is the total amount of money Simone spent?

T: _____

I: _____

_____

N: _____

S: _____

_____

WORK SPACE

Addition and Subtraction Mixed Review: Take the Challenge II

Use TINS to solve the following word problems. Remember to draw pictures, circle key words, and cross out extra information.

---

1. During the fall Mrs. Owen's class read 20 books. Mrs. Nolle's class read 10 books. How many more books did Mrs. Owen's class read?

Thought: _____

Information: _____

_____

Number Sentence: _____

Solution Sentence: _____

_____

WORK SPACE

---

2. Victoria has 17 posters and Gabby has 15 posters. How many more posters does Victoria have?

T: _____

I: _____

_____

N: _____

S: _____

_____

WORK SPACE

3. Dolores earns $103.75 baby-sitting in July and $87.65 baby-sitting in August. How much money does Dolores earn in all?

T: _____

I: _____

_____

N: _____

S: _____

_____

WORK SPACE

---

4. A thirsty camel drank 28 gallons of water in the early morning. The camel drinks an additional 10 gallons of water at noon. How much water did the camel drink in all?

T: _____

I: _____

_____

N: _____

S: _____

_____

WORK SPACE

5. Miguel's dog chewed 5 bones in May, 4 bones in September, and 9 bones in October. How many bones did Miguel's dog chew in September and October?

T: _____

I: _____

_____

N: _____

S: _____

_____

WORK SPACE

6. Camilla went to the mall on her birthday. Her dad gave her $25 to spend. She bought a new skirt for $19. How much money does Camilla have left?

T: _____

I: _____

_____

N: _____

S: _____

_____

WORK SPACE

7. Gaylon has 7 compact disks (CDs) in his music collection. Mateo has 8 CDs in his collection. Gaylon receives 4 new CDs for his birthday. How many CDs does Gaylon have now?

T: _____

I: _____

_____

N: _____

S: _____

_____

WORK SPACE

8. Jasmine picked 14 flowers. She gave 11 away. How many flowers does she have left?

T: _____

I: _____

_____

N: _____

S: _____

_____

WORK SPACE

9. At Goodhealth Elementary there are 4 students lined up for the relay race. There are an additional 8 students waiting to run in the race. How many will run in all?

T: _____

I: _____

_____

N: _____

S: _____

_____

WORK SPACE

10. The track team ran 11 miles on Monday, 6 miles on Tuesday, and 7 miles on Wednesday. How many more miles did the track team run on Monday than on Wednesday?

T: _____

I: _____

_____

N: _____

S: _____

_____

WORK SPACE

11. The Nisimblats traveled 233 miles on Saturday and 345 miles on Sunday. How many more miles did they travel on Sunday?

T: _____

I: _____

_____

N: _____

S: _____

_____

WORK SPACE

12. Eight people are meeting in the Green Room at the Canoe Club. There are eleven people meeting in the Canoe Club's Blue Room. How many people are using the Blue and Green Rooms at the Canoe Club?

T: _____

I: _____

_____

N: _____

S: _____

_____

WORK SPACE

13. Before the bus started down Oak Street, it was filled with 9 students. When it pulled away from the curb on Vine Street, there were 16 passengers on the bus. How many students entered the bus between Oak and Vine Streets?

T: _____

I: _____

_____

N: _____

S: _____

_____

WORK SPACE

14. The gardener spotted 3 yellow caterpillars, 2 butterflies, 8 ladybugs, and 2 bumblebees in Wilson Park on Wednesday. How many insects did the gardener see in Wilson Park on Wednesday?

T: _____

I: _____

_____

N: _____

S: _____

_____

WORK SPACE

15. Mr. Ogle has $29. He spends $14 on a baseball cap. How much money does he have now?

T: _____

I: _____

_____

N: _____

S: _____

_____

WORK SPACE

16. Michelle enjoys whale watching. At the aquarium she learns that a whale's heart usually beats 9 times every minute. Michelle timed her own heart and found it beats 70 times every minute. How many more times each minute does Michelle's heart beat?

T: _____

I: _____

_____

N: _____

S: _____

_____

WORK SPACE

17. Lane spends 7 hours fishing with his dad on Saturday and 9 hours fishing with his dad on Sunday. How many more hours did he spend fishing Sunday?

T: _____

I: _____

_____

N: _____

S: _____

_____

WORK SPACE

18. The Bedford Amusement Park recently built a drawbridge. When the bridge opens upward, each side is 48 feet long. How long is the entire bridge?

T: _____

I: _____

_____

N: _____

S: _____

_____

WORK SPACE

19. Tom has 10 marbles. Dave gave Tom
2 marbles. How many marbles does Tom have?

T: _____

I: _____

_____

N: _____

S: _____

_____

WORK SPACE

20. Margery went to the Farmer's Market on
Saturday. She bought 16 jars of jam, 9 apples,
4 oranges, and 2 pineapples. How many pieces
of fruit did Margery buy in all?

T: _____

I: _____

_____

N: _____

S: _____

_____

WORK SPACE

Write Your Own I

Use the information provided to write your own addition or subtraction word problems. Then use TINS to solve each problem. Challenge your friends to solve some of the problems you create!

Example: Phoebe has $15. She spent $6.

Question: Phoebe has $15. She spent $6 on a new headband. How much money does Phoebe have left?

Thought: _____ — _____

Information: $15 in pocket, $6 headband

Number Sentence: $15 — $6 =

Solution Sentence: Phoebe has $9 left.

WORK SPACE

---

1. Bernadette has 9 baseball cards. She sells 4 baseball cards.

Question: _____

_____

Thought: _____

Information: _____

_____

Number Sentence: _____

Solution Sentence: _____

_____

WORK SPACE

2. Deirdre has $43. Maria has $17.

Question: _____

_____

T: _____

I: _____

_____

N: _____

S: _____

_____

WORK SPACE

---

3. Jose bought 19 postcards. He mailed 8.

Question: _____

_____

T: _____

I: _____

_____

N: _____

S: _____

_____

WORK SPACE

4. Martin makes $9 mowing the yard. He later earns $16.

Question: _____

_____

T: _____

I: _____

_____

N: _____

S: _____

_____

WORK SPACE

---

5. The language lab has 15 headsets. The Spanish class has 17 students.

Question: _____

_____

T: _____

I: _____

_____

N: _____

S: _____

_____

WORK SPACE

Write Your Own II

Write your own addition or subtraction word problems. Then use TINS to solve them. Remember to draw a picture, circle key words, and cross out information that isn't important. Happy problem writing!

1. Question: _____

_____

Thought: _____

Information: _____

_____

Number Sentence: _____

Solution Sentence: _____

_____

WORK SPACE

2. Question: _____

_____

T: _____

I: _____

_____

N: _____

S: _____

_____

WORK SPACE

3. Question: _____

_____

T: _____

I: _____

_____

N: _____

S: _____

_____

WORK SPACE

---

4. Question: _____

_____

T: _____

I: _____

_____

N: _____

S: _____

_____

WORK SPACE

5. Question: _____

_____

T: _____

I: _____

_____

N: _____

S: _____

_____

WORK SPACE

6. Question: _____

_____

T: _____

I: _____

_____

N: _____

S: _____

_____

WORK SPACE

Explain

Use TINS to solve each word problem. Then write at least 2 sentences explaining how you solved the problem.

Example: There were 21 fish swimming in a school. Six fish swam away. How many fish are left in the school?

WORK SPACE

Thought: _____

Information: _21 fish swimming, 6 swam_

away

Number Sentence: _21 – 6 =_

Solution Sentence: _There are 15 fish left_

swimming in the school.

Explanation: _I know that 6 fish are left._

So the number of fish in the school

will decrease by 6.

1. Jeffrey saved $187 in third grade, $232.75 in fourth grade and $98 in fifth grade. What is the total amount of money Jeffrey saved during this three-year period?

Thought: _____

Information: _____

_____

Number Sentence: _____

Solution Sentence: _____

_____

Explanation: _____

_____

_____

WORK SPACE

2. Ron spent 25 minutes cleaning his fish bowl. Karen spent 40 minutes walking and brushing her dog. How much longer did Karen take than Ron?

T: _____

I: _____

_____

N: _____

S: _____

_____

Explanation: _____

_____

_____

WORK SPACE

3. An actor arrived at the studio at 3:05 P.M. The show starts at 3:30 P.M. How much time does the actor have to get ready?

Thought: _____

Information: _____

_____

Number Sentence: _____

Solution Sentence: _____

_____

Explanation: _____

_____

_____

WORK SPACE

---

4. Mary is a fashion buyer for a clothing store. She decides to order 20 dresses of style A and 10 dresses of style B. What is the total number of dresses Mary orders?

Thought: _____

Information: _____

_____

Number Sentence: _____

Solution Sentence: _____

_____

Explanation: _____

_____

_____

WORK SPACE

More Addition and Subtraction Mixed Review

Use TINS to solve the following word problems. Remember to draw pictures, circle key words, and cross out extra information.

1. Rosetta found 9 shells at the seashore. She took 2 shells home for her fish tank. How many did she leave behind?

Thought: _____

Information: _____

_____

Number Sentence: _____

Solution Sentence: _____

_____

WORK SPACE

2. Philippe took 5 white shirts, 3 blue shirts, and 2 yellow shirts to the dry cleaner. How many more blue shirts than yellow shirts did Philippe take to the cleaner?

T: _____

I: _____

_____

N: _____

S: _____

_____

WORK SPACE

3. Trudy has 6 goldfish, 3 cats, and 2 dogs. She gave 3 goldfish to her cousin. How many goldfish does Trudy have now?

T: _____

I: _____

_____

N: _____

S: _____

_____

WORK SPACE

4. John and Harry are driving 150 miles to Boston. They have already driven 50 miles. How many more miles do they have left to travel?

T: _____

I: _____

_____

N: _____

S: _____

_____

WORK SPACE

5. Bates Elementary created a banner for all students to sign on the first day of school. On the morning of the first day of school 564 students signed the banner and 289 students signed the banner in the afternoon. How many students signed the banner on the first day of school?

WORK SPACE

T: _____

I: _____

_____

N: _____

S: _____

_____

6. Mrs. Rodriques has 23 students in her class, Mr. Costa has 25 students in his class, and Mrs. Gomes has 19 students in her class. How many students do the three teachers have altogether?

WORK SPACE

T: _____

I: _____

_____

N: _____

S: _____

_____

7. The circus sold 1,001 tickets for its first performance and 985 tickets for its second performance. How many more tickets did the circus sell for its first performance?

T: _____

I: _____

_____

N: _____

S: _____

_____

WORK SPACE

8. Leroy has 63 bones in his arms and legs, 29 in his skull, 26 in his spine, and 25 in his chest. How many bones are in Leroy's body?

T: _____

I: _____

_____

N: _____

S: _____

_____

WORK SPACE

9. Tanya drew the American flag with 50 stars and 13 stripes. How many stars and stripes does her flag have altogether?

T: _____

I: _____

_____

N: _____

S: _____

_____

WORK SPACE

10. Rosa spent $14.50 mailing letters the first week she was at camp and $22.93 mailing letters and packages the second week she was at camp. What is the total amount of money Rosa spent mailing things during the two weeks she was at camp?

T: _____

I: _____

_____

N: _____

S: _____

_____

WORK SPACE

11. Desiree's family drove 189 miles on the first day of vacation, 232 miles on the second day of vacation, and 111 miles on the third day of vacation. How many miles did Desiree's family drive on the first two days of vacation?

T: _____

I: _____

_____

N: _____

S: _____

_____

WORK SPACE

12. Julie bought 2 red barrettes, 7 green barrettes, and 9 orange barrettes at the store. How many green and red barrettes did Julie buy in all?

T: _____

I: _____

_____

N: _____

S: _____

_____

WORK SPACE

13. A pine tree grew 5 inches in April and 3 inches in May. How many more inches did the Pine tree grow in April than in May?

T: _____

I: _____

_____

N: _____

S: _____

_____

WORK SPACE

14. Solomon was landscaping his grandmother's yard. He planted 15 small trees and 43 flowers. How many plants did Solomon use in all?

T: _____

I: _____

_____

N: _____

S: _____

_____

WORK SPACE

15. It takes 17 muscles for Mary Beth to smile and 43 muscles to frown. How many more muscles does it take her to frown?

T: _____

I: _____

_____

N: _____

S: _____

_____

WORK SPACE

16. The Ravin' Rock Group is going on tour. They plan on traveling 898 miles the first week, 1,600 miles the second week, and 1,001 miles the third week. How many more miles will the rock group travel the second week than the first week?

T: _____

I: _____

_____

N: _____

S: _____

_____

WORK SPACE

17. Caleb ran for 56 minutes on Saturday and 43 minutes on Sunday. Each day he eats 2 bananas before he goes running. How many more minutes did Caleb run Saturday?

T: _____

I: _____

_____

N: _____

S: _____

_____

WORK SPACE

18. Martina started an exercise journal to keep track of the miles she walks each week. Her journal showed that she walked 23 miles the first week, 35 miles the second week, and 44 miles the third week. What was the total number of miles she walked in three weeks?

T: _____

I: _____

_____

N: _____

S: _____

_____

WORK SPACE

19. Theresa's family is taking the bus to visit her grandparents. It costs $63 each for Theresa and her brother to ride the bus. It costs $102 for their mother and $87 for Aunt Louisa. What is the total cost for Theresa's family of four to ride the bus?

T: _____

I: _____

_____

N: _____

S: _____

_____

WORK SPACE

20. During the summer months there were 54 sunny days, 32 rainy days, and 11 cloudy days. How many days were there in the summer when it did not rain?

T: _____

I: _____

_____

N: _____

S: _____

_____

WORK SPACE

Solving Multiplication Word Problems with TINS

Are multiplication word problems getting you down? Get ready to shine: TINS is here! Below are some key words that appear in multiplication word problems.

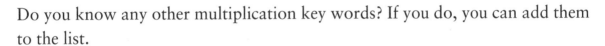

🔑 groups   (and other words that are kinds of groups)
                   Examples: groups of campers, batches of cookies, bunches
                   of grapes, bags of groceries, litters of kittens

🔑 each   Each is a tricky key word because it shows up in division
                   problems, too. You'll know you are most likely reading a
                   multiplication problem if each shows up with one of its buddies:
                   altogether, in all, or total.

Do you know any other multiplication key words? If you do, you can add them to the list.

When you see a multiplication key word in a problem, circle it and write x above the key word. Then write x on the THOUGHT line. Next, circle and write down the important INFORMATION from the word problem. Sometimes it helps to draw a picture of the important information. Now write your information as a NUMBER SENTENCE. Then plug your answer into your SOLUTION SENTENCE.

Example: Rosalie baked (4 batches) of muffin. There were (6 muffins in each batch). How many muffins did Rosalie bake (in all)?

Thought: _____ x _____

Information: __4 batches, 6 in each batch__

_____

Number Sentence: __4 x 6 = _____

Solution Sentence: __Rosalie baked__

__24 muffins in all.__

WORK SPACE

Try It Out

Use TINS to solve these word problems. Remember to circle key words and draw pictures. The first 4 problems have pictures to help you.

---

1. Samantha has 4 green shirts. She wants to replace all of the buttons on these shirts. If each shirt has 3 buttons, how many buttons will she need?

Thought: _____

Information: _____

_____

Number Sentence: _____

Solution Sentence: _____

_____

WORK SPACE

---

2. Sierra has a sticker collection. Her book can hold 10 stickers on each page. How many total stickers does she have on 5 pages?

T: _____

I: _____

_____

N: _____

S: _____

_____

WORK SPACE

3. Rita has 6 sisters. Each sister has exactly 4 children. How many nieces and nephews does Rita have?

T: _____

I: _____

_____

N: _____

S: _____

_____

WORK SPACE

4. Mr. Pina subscribed to 4 different magazines. At the end of the year he will have received 12 issues of each magazine. How many magazines will he have?

T: _____

I: _____

_____

N: _____

S: _____

_____

WORK SPACE

5. The elephant-shaped house in Margate, New Jersey has 8 rooms. If each room has two windows, how many windows are in the house?

WORK SPACE

T: _____

I: _____

_____

N: _____

S: _____

_____

6. A popular television show is on 5 days every week. The show is 2 hours long. How many hours is the show on during the week?

WORK SPACE

T: _____

I: _____

_____

N: _____

S: _____

_____

7. Three brothers saved $25 each. What is the total amount of money the three brothers saved?

T: _____

I: _____

_____

N: _____

S: _____

_____

WORK SPACE

---

8. Each morning Cecile, Carmen, and Kathy walk a total of 6 blocks before they reach the bus stop. How many blocks do they pass altogether in 5 mornings?

T: _____

I: _____

_____

N: _____

S: _____

_____

WORK SPACE

9. It costs Mr. Longo $128 each month to ride the train to work. How much money will he have to pay if he rides the train for 3 months?

T: _____

I: _____

_____

N: _____

S: _____

_____

WORK SPACE

10. The movie theater has 15 rows of seats. Each row has 6 seats in it. The movie theater shows 4 movies every day. How many seats does the movie theater have?

T: _____

I: _____

_____

N: _____

S: _____

_____

WORK SPACE

On Your Own

Use TINS to solve these word problems. Remember to circle key words and draw pictures.

1. Sam has 10 tickets to sell for the charity raffle. Each ticket costs $5. If Sam sells every ticket, how much money will he have raised for charity?

Thought: _____

Information: _____

_____

Number Sentence: _____

Solution Sentence: _____

_____

WORK SPACE

2. Mrs. Kaplan bought 3 bags of peanuts. Each bag contains 10 peanuts. How many peanuts does she have in all?

T: _____

I: _____

_____

N: _____

S: _____

_____

WORK SPACE

3. Sarah has 7 shirts. She wants to replace 3 buttons on each shirt. How many buttons should she buy?

T: _____

I: _____

_____

N: _____

S: _____

_____

WORK SPACE

---

4. Bill's plant had 5 hours of sunlight each day for 7 days. How many hours of sunlight did the plant receive that week?

T: _____

I: _____

_____

N: _____

S: _____

_____

WORK SPACE

5. Jocelyn works on her needlepoint 15 minutes every night. If she works for 6 nights, what is the total amount of time Jocelyn spends on her needlepoint?

T: _____

I: _____

_____

N: _____

S: _____

_____

WORK SPACE

6. Danielle blinks 22 times each minute. How many times will Danielle blink after 4 minutes?

T: _____

I: _____

_____

N: _____

S: _____

_____

WORK SPACE

7. Raymond runs 27 miles a week. What is the total number of miles Raymond runs in four weeks?

T: _____

I: _____

_____

N: _____

S: _____

_____

WORK SPACE

8. Samantha earns $12 for her weekly allowance. Last month she took out the trash 11 times. How much money did Samantha earn after three weeks?

T: _____

I: _____

_____

N: _____

S: _____

_____

WORK SPACE

9. The Angels played six baseball games during the past two weeks. Seventy-five people attended each game. The Angels won 5 out of the 6 games. What was the total number of people that attended all six baseball games?

T: _____

I: _____

_____

N: _____

S: _____

_____

WORK SPACE

10. Mr. Correia breeds show dogs. He currently has four dogs. Each dog has ten puppies. How many puppies in all?

T: _____

I: _____

_____

N: _____

S: _____

_____

WORK SPACE

Take the Challenge

Make a list of the multiplication key words you know.

_____

_____

Remember to look for these words as you use TINS to solve the problems below. Re-check each solution sentence to make sure it makes sense.

1. Maria travels a total of 25 miles to and from school each day. What is the total number of miles Maria travels in 5 days?

Thought: _____

Information: _____

_____

Number Sentence: _____

Solution Sentence: _____

_____

WORK SPACE

2. Joel invited three friends over to play golf. Each boy brought five golf balls. How many golf balls did Joel's friends bring?

T: _____

I: _____

_____

N: _____

S: _____

_____

WORK SPACE

3. Monica plants 2 rows of tomato plants. She places 4 plants in each row. How many tomato plants does Monica plant in all?

T: _____

I: _____

_____

N: _____

S: _____

_____

WORK SPACE

4. Victor bought 6 light bulbs. Each bulb will last 750 hours. How many hours will all his light bulbs last?

T: _____

I: _____

_____

N: _____

S: _____

_____

WORK SPACE

5. Roberta's elementary school has three smoke detectors in every hallway. There are seven hallways in the entire school. How many smoke detectors does Roberta's school have in all?

T: _____

I: _____

_____

N: _____

S: _____

_____

WORK SPACE

6. Leo spent 3 days learning to play chopsticks on the piano. He practiced every day for 45 minutes each day. How many minutes did he practice chopsticks?

T: _____

I: _____

_____

N: _____

S: _____

_____

WORK SPACE

7. Francisco spent five hours a day painting his house. How many hours did Francisco spend painting if he worked for a total of nine days?

T: _____

I: _____

_____

N: _____

S: _____

_____

WORK SPACE

8. Louisa bought 16 pens. Each pen costs $3. How much money did Louisa spend on pens?

T: _____

I: _____

_____

N: _____

S: _____

_____

WORK SPACE

9. Luther traveled 250 miles a day for 3 straight days. How many miles did he travel in all?

T: _____

I: _____

_____

N: _____

S: _____

_____

WORK SPACE

10. Dominique earns $15 a day for five days in a row. What are his total earnings for all five days?

T: _____

I: _____

_____

N: _____

S: _____

_____

WORK SPACE

11. Marsha sent two e-mail messages to each of her nine friends. How many e-mails did Marsha send in all?

T: _____

I: _____

_____

N: _____

S: _____

_____

WORK SPACE

12. President Andrew Jackson's picture appears on the $20 bill. Roberto has collected 10 bills with Jackson's picture. How much money does Roberto have in all?

T: _____

I: _____

_____

N: _____

S: _____

_____

WORK SPACE

13. Venus passes between the Earth and the Sun every 584 days. How many days have gone by if the earth and sun pass 5 times?

T: _____

I: _____

_____

N: _____

S: _____

_____

WORK SPACE

14. Mrs. Maloney bought three bouquets of flowers for her apartment. Each bouquet contains twenty flowers in all. How many flowers does Mrs. Maloney have in her apartment?

T: _____

I: _____

_____

N: _____

S: _____

_____

WORK SPACE

15. J.J. plans on reading 55 pages of his book every night for a total of three nights. What is the total number of pages J.J. will read?

T: _____

I: _____

_____

N: _____

S: _____

_____

WORK SPACE

16. Renee checked out 3 library books every week for 15 weeks. How many library books did Renee check out?

T: _____

I: _____

_____

N: _____

S: _____

_____

WORK SPACE

17. Ms. Birnbaum has six easels in the art room. Each easel has ten paintbrushes and two cups of water attached to it. What is the total number of paintbrushes on all six easels?

T: _____

I: _____

_____

N: _____

S: _____

_____

WORK SPACE

18. Tito the Elephant drank 50 gallons of water in one night. How many gallons of water will Tito drink in 8 nights if he continues to drink the same amount of water each night?

T: _____

I: _____

_____

N: _____

S: _____

_____

WORK SPACE

---

19. Timothy bought one bracelet for each of his three sisters. He spent $8.20 on each bracelet. What is the total amount Timothy spent on bracelets?

T: _____

I: _____

_____

N: _____

S: _____

_____

WORK SPACE

20. Leona loves orange juice. She drinks four glasses of orange juice for breakfast every morning. How many glasses of orange juice will Leona drink in three days?

T: _____

I: _____

_____

N: _____

S: _____

_____

WORK SPACE

---

21. Craig has 57 CDs in his collection. He wants to take as many as he can on vacation. His CD wallet has 12 pages. Each page holds 4 CDs. How many CDs can Craig take with him?

T: _____

I: _____

_____

N: _____

S: _____

_____

WORK SPACE

Write Your Own I

Use the information provided to write your own multiplication word problems. Use TINS to solve each problem. Challenge your friends to solve some of the problems you create!

Example: Hsi-Chang has 4 plates of cookies. There are seven cookies on each plate.

Question: Hsi-Chang baked oatmeal raisin cookies. He put (seven cookies) on (four) different plates. How many oatmeal raisin cookies does Hsi-Chang have (in all)?

Thought: _____ x _____

Information: _7 cookies, 4 plates_

Number Sentence: _7 x 4 =_

Solution Sentence: _Hsi-chang has_
28 oatmeal cookies in all.

WORK SPACE

---

1. Johanna has four cats. Each cat has two bells on its collar.

Question: _____

_____

Thought: _____

Information: _____

_____

Number Sentence: _____

Solution Sentence: _____

_____

WORK SPACE

2. Oscar fishes for sixteen days. He catches five fish each day.

Question: _____

_____

T: _____

I: _____

_____

N: _____

S: _____

_____

WORK SPACE

---

3. Liam practices football for five days each week. Practice lasts three hours.

Question: _____

_____

T: _____

I: _____

_____

N: _____

S: _____

_____

WORK SPACE

4. Three friends go to the fair. Each friend spends $18.

Question: _____

_____

T: _____

I: _____

_____

N: _____

S: _____

_____

WORK SPACE

5. Each member of the rugby team has two shirts, one for home games and one for away games. There are sixteen rugby team members.

Question: _____

_____

T: _____

I: _____

_____

N: _____

S: _____

_____

WORK SPACE

Write Your Own II

Write your own multiplication word problems. Use TINS to solve them. Remember to draw pictures and circle key words. Happy problem writing!

---

1. Question: _____

_____

T: _____

I: _____

_____

N: _____

S: _____

_____

---

2. Question: _____

_____

T: _____

I: _____

_____

N: _____

S: _____

_____

3. Question: _____

_____

T: _____

I: _____

_____

N: _____

S: _____

_____

WORK SPACE

4. Question: _____

_____

T: _____

I: _____

_____

N: _____

S: _____

_____

WORK SPACE

5. Question: _____

_____

T: _____

I: _____

_____

N: _____

S: _____

_____

WORK SPACE

6. Question: _____

_____

T: _____

I: _____

_____

N: _____

S: _____

_____

WORK SPACE

Explain

Use TINS to solve each word problem. Then write at least 2 sentences explaining how you solved the problem.

Example: Ortella and Susanna often go to the movies. Their favorite movie theater has 6 rows of seats and each row has 9 seats. What is the total number of seats in the movie theater?

Thought: _____ x _____

Information: _6 rows of seats, 9 seats in_

_each row_____

Number Sentence: _6 x 9 =_____

Solution Sentence: _There are 54 seats_

_in the movie theater._____

Explanation: _I know the theater has_

6 groups of 9, so I need to multiply.

When I drew a picture, I saw that the

_theater has 54 seats._____

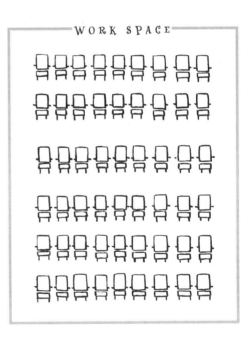

WORK SPACE

1. Beth bought a small photo album with 8 pages. She can fit 2 pictures on one page. How many pictures can she fit in the album?

Thought: _____

Information: _____

_____

Number Sentence: _____

Solution Sentence: _____

_____

Explanation: _____

_____

```
┌──────── W O R K   S P A C E ────────┐
│                                     │
│                                     │
│                                     │
│                                     │
│                                     │
│                                     │
│                                     │
│                                     │
│                                     │
└─────────────────────────────────────┘
```

2. Monica bought 8 stamps. Each stamp cost her 33 cents. How much did Monica spend?

T: _____

I: _____

_____

N: _____

S: _____

_____

Explanation: _____

_____

```
┌──────── W O R K   S P A C E ────────┐
│                                     │
│                                     │
│                                     │
│                                     │
│                                     │
│                                     │
│                                     │
│                                     │
│                                     │
└─────────────────────────────────────┘
```

Solving Division Word Problems with TINS

If TINS can help you with addition, subtraction, and multiplication word problems, then—you guessed it! TINS can help you achieve your goal in division word problems, too. Check out these division key words.

- each
- separate
- quotient
- equal
- divide
- equally

Each is that pesky key word that also appears in multiplication word problems. If each appears with another division key word, such as divide or equally, then you're probably dealing with a division problem.

Can you think of any other division key words? If so, add them to the list.

When you see a division key word in a problem, circle it and write ÷ above the key word. Then write ÷ on the Thought line. Next, circle and write down the important Information from the word problem. Sometimes it helps to draw a picture of the important information. Now write your information as a Number Sentence. Then plug your answer into your Solution Sentence.

Example: Molly has 15 teddy bears. She wants to share the bears equally between herself, Elizabeth, and Will. How many teddy bears will each person get?

Thought: _____ ÷ _____

Information: 15 teddy bears, 3 people

_____

Number Sentence: 15 ÷ 3 =

Solution Sentence: Each person will get 5 bears.

WORK SPACE

Try It Out

Use TINS to solve these word problems. Remember to circle key words and draw pictures. The first 4 problems have pictures to help you.

1. Maxine has four pounds of sugar. She needs to divide the sugar equally between four different recipes. How many pounds of sugar will each recipe have?

Thought: _____

Information: _____

_____

Number Sentence: _____

Solution Sentence: _____

_____

WORK SPACE

2. If the moon takes 28 days to revolve around the earth, how many days would it take to revolve half way around the earth?

T: _____

I: _____

_____

N: _____

S: _____

_____

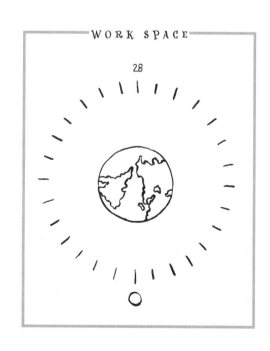

WORK SPACE

28

3. Twenty students attend tutoring classes after school. There are five students in each group. How many groups are there in all?

WORK SPACE

T: _____

I: _____

_____

N: _____

S: _____

_____

4. Bryant was one of six finalists at a cooking contest. He submitted a total of 45 copies of his menus to the 9 judges. How many copies did each judge receive?

WORK SPACE

T: _____

I: _____

_____

N: _____

S: _____

_____

5. The 60 entrants in a milk-drinking contest were separated into 3 divisions. How many milk drinkers were in each division?

WORK SPACE

T: _____

I: _____

_____

N: _____

S: _____

_____

6. A farmer's bamboo grass grew 3 feet in one day. At this rate, how many days will it take the grass to grow 15 feet?

WORK SPACE

T: _____

I: _____

_____

N: _____

S: _____

_____

7. An ostrich can produce an egg that is large enough to feed 12 people. How many eggs would an ostrich need to produce to feed 48 people?

T: _____

I: _____

_____

N: _____

S: _____

_____

WORK SPACE

8. Grandpa Barrows has 1,000 photographs. The photo shop scanned all of the pictures onto 5 compact disks. If each disk contains the same number of photos, how many pictures are on each CD?

T: _____

I: _____

_____

N: _____

S: _____

_____

WORK SPACE

9. Mr. Jones bought 88 baseball cards. He divided the cards equally between his daughter and son. How many cards did each receive?

T: _____

I: _____

_____

N: _____

S: _____

_____

WORK SPACE

---

10. Five cats have to share 150 catnips. How many catnips will each cat receive?

T: _____

I: _____

_____

N: _____

S: _____

_____

WORK SPACE

Take the Challenge I

Make a list of the division key words you know.

_____

_____

Remember to look for these words as you use TINS to solve the problems below. Re-check each solution sentence to make sure it makes sense!

1. Tammy has 24 flowers. She wants to divide an equal number between herself and 3 friends. How many flowers will each girl receive?

Thought: _____

Information: _____

_____

Number Sentence: _____

Solution Sentence: _____

_____

```
┌──────── WORK SPACE ────────┐
│                            │
│                            │
│                            │
│                            │
│                            │
│                            │
│                            │
│                            │
└────────────────────────────┘
```

2. Ted has collected 30 shells. He wants to display them in three separate jars. How many shells will Ted put in each jar?

T: _____

I: _____

_____

N: _____

S: _____

_____

```
┌──────── WORK SPACE ────────┐
│                            │
│                            │
│                            │
│                            │
│                            │
│                            │
│                            │
│                            │
└────────────────────────────┘
```

3. Leo circled an old elm tree 3 times on Wednesday. It took him a total of 21 steps. How many steps did it take Leo to circle the tree once?

T: _____

I: _____

_____

N: _____

S: _____

_____

WORK SPACE

4. Damien orders six presents and he spends a total of $72. Each present costs the same amount. How much did each present cost?

T: _____

I: _____

_____

N: _____

S: _____

_____

WORK SPACE

5. The librarian buys fifty new books for the library. She wants to put ten books on each bookshelf. How many bookshelves will the librarian use?

T: _____

I: _____

_____

N: _____

S: _____

_____

WORK SPACE

6. Bianca went to the beach on her vacation. She spent a total of $150 during the five days she was gone. She spent the same amount of money each day she was away. How much money did Bianca spend each day she was at the beach?

T: _____

I: _____

_____

N: _____

S: _____

_____

WORK SPACE

7. Joe bought 18 new golf balls. He wants to divide the golf balls equally between three pockets in his golf bag. How many balls will he place in each pocket?

T: _____

I: _____

_____

N: _____

S: _____

_____

WORK SPACE

---

8. Four shuttle buses are scheduled to take five hundred students home. The bus drivers want to divide the students equally between the four buses. How many students will ride on each bus?

T: _____

I: _____

_____

N: _____

S: _____

_____

WORK SPACE

9. Three friends go out to lunch. The bill for lunch is $33. Each friend owes the same amount of money. How much money does each friend owe?

T: _____

I: _____

_____

N: _____

S: _____

_____

WORK SPACE

---

10. A baker bakes 81 apple turnovers. She plans to let the turnovers cool on 9 platters. How many turnovers will be on each platter?

T: _____

I: _____

_____

N: _____

S: _____

_____

WORK SPACE

Division Word Problems: Take the Challenge II

Circle key words, draw pictures, and use TINS to solve the following problems.

1. Lorenzo, Joseph, and Antonio went fishing. They caught twenty-four fish. Each boy caught an equal number of fish. How many fish did each boy catch?

Thought: _____

Information: _____

_____

Number Sentence: _____

Solution Sentence: _____

_____

WORK SPACE

2. Forty-nine newspapers were delivered to seven houses during the week. If an equal number of newspapers were delivered to each house how many newspapers did each house receive?

T: _____

I: _____

_____

N: _____

S: _____

_____

WORK SPACE

3. The Calswell family spent a total of $128 buying food and drinks for the family BBQ. The four hosts of the party plan to divide the bill equally. How much does each host owe?

T: _____

I: _____

_____

N: _____

S: _____

_____

WORK SPACE

---

4. Mrs. Wells picked twenty-five apples to share between herself and her four sons. How many apples will each person get if they share the apples equally?

T: _____

I: _____

_____

N: _____

S: _____

_____

WORK SPACE

5. The girl's basketball team spends $450 on new uniforms. Nine players divide this amount equally. How much does each player owe?

T: _____

I: _____

_____

N: _____

S: _____

_____

WORK SPACE

6. Will has six pieces of chalk. He divides them equally between Todd and M.J. How many pieces of chalk does each person get?

T: _____

I: _____

_____

N: _____

S: _____

_____

WORK SPACE

7. After 42 green apples ripen to red, farmer Frank places the apples in 6 boxes. How many red apples are divided into each box?

T: _____

I: _____

_____

N: _____

S: _____

_____

WORK SPACE

---

8. Rosco the magician arranges 6 boxes on 2 tables. He has a total of 18 cotton rabbits to put in the boxes. If the rabbits are equally divided between each box, how many rabbits will Rosco pull out of each box?

T: _____

I: _____

_____

N: _____

S: _____

_____

WORK SPACE

9. The Martinez family drove a total of ninety-nine miles on their three-day vacation last summer. They drove an equal number of miles each day. How many miles did they drive each day?

T: _____

I: _____

_____

N: _____

S: _____

_____

10. Ten contestants enter an apple pie eating contest. They eat sixty apple pies. If each contestant eats an equal number of pies how many pies does each contestant eat?

T: _____

I: _____

_____

N: _____

S: _____

_____

Write Your Own I

Use the information provided to write your own division word problems. Then use TINS to solve each problem. Challenge your friends to solve some of the problems you create!

Example: Matt has 18 hockey pucks. He shares them with 3 friends.

Question: Matt buys 18 hockey pucks. He wants to give an equal number of pucks to Jeff, Rob, and Jesse. How many pucks will each friend receive?

Thought: _____ ÷ _____

Information: __18 hockey pucks, 3 friends__

_____

Number Sentence: _____18 ÷ 3 = _____

Solution Sentence: ___Matt gives each___

_____friend 6 hockey pucks.___

```
━━━━━━ WORK SPACE ━━━━━━




```

1. $100 was given to two boys. They spent it.

Question: _____

_____

Thought: _____

Information: _____

_____

Number Sentence: _____

Solution Sentence: _____

_____

WORK SPACE

---

2. Fourteen chairs are in a classroom. Two chairs are at each desk.

Question: _____

_____

T: _____

I: _____

_____

N: _____

S: _____

_____

WORK SPACE

3. Twenty-seven messages. There are nine time capsules.

Question: _____

_____

T: _____

I: _____

_____

N: _____

S: _____

_____

WORK SPACE

4. There are one hundred students at Jonah's elementary school. Twenty students are in each class.

Question: _____

_____

T: _____

I: _____

_____

N: _____

S: _____

_____

WORK SPACE

Write Your Own II

Write your own division word problems. Then use TINS to solve them.
Remember to draw pictures and circle key words. Happy problem writing!

1. Question: _____

_____

Thought: _____

Information: _____

_____

Number Sentence: _____

Solution Sentence: _____

_____

WORK SPACE

2. Question: _____

_____

_____

T: _____

I: _____

_____

N: _____

S: _____

_____

WORK SPACE

3. Question: _____

_____

_____

T: _____

I: _____

_____

N: _____

S: _____

_____

4. Question: _____

_____

_____

T: _____

I: _____

_____

N: _____

S: _____

_____

5. Question: _____

_____

_____

T: _____

I: _____

_____

N: _____

S: _____

_____

Explain

Use TINS to solve each word problem. Then write at least 2 sentences explaining how you solved the problem.

Example: Mr. Knowles has 24 plants. He wants to put 6 plants in each box. How many boxes does he need?

Thought: _____ ÷ _____

Information: _____24 plants, 6 plants_____
_____in each box_____

Number Sentence: _____24 ÷ 6 = _____

Solution Sentence: Mr. Knowles will need
_____4 boxes._____

Explanation: I know that Mr. Knowles wants
6 plants in each group. When I divide
the 24 plants so that there are 6 in
each group, I see that he needs
4 boxes.

> **WORK SPACE**

1. Domingo spent $10 on one box of floppy disks. If there are 10 disks in the box, how much money did Domingo spend for one disk?

Thought: _____

Information: _____

_____

Number Sentence: _____

Solution Sentence: _____

_____

Explanation: _____

_____

_____

WORK SPACE

---

2. If a 15-foot roll of plaid ribbon is cut into 5 equal pieces, about how long would each piece be?

T: _____

I: _____

_____

N: _____

S: _____

_____

Explanation: _____

_____

_____

WORK SPACE

Multiplication and Division Mixed Review

Use TINS to solve these problems. Remember to circle key words and draw pictures.

1. Melanie had sixteen envelopes. She placed two stamps on each envelope. How many stamps did Melanie use in all?

Thought: _____

Information: _____

_____

Number Sentence: _____

Solution Sentence: _____

_____

WORK SPACE

2. Tyrone has twenty-four pens. He wants to put his pens in six supply boxes. How many supply boxes will he need to store his pens?

T: _____

I: _____

_____

N: _____

S: _____

_____

WORK SPACE

3. Virginia hangs three sets of pictures on six different walls in her apartment. How many total pictures does she hang in all?

T: _____

I: _____

_____

N: _____

S: _____

_____

WORK SPACE

4. A Ferris wheel has 12 passenger cars. Each car can hold 3 riders. How many passengers can ride the wheel if all the seats are taken?

T: _____

I: _____

_____

N: _____

S: _____

_____

WORK SPACE

5. Six bluejays lay twenty eggs each. How many eggs do the bluejays lay in all?

T: _____

I: _____

_____

N: _____

S: _____

_____

WORK SPACE

---

6. There are 72 rooms on 9 floors of the Eastside Office Complex. The same number of rooms is on each floor. How many rooms are there on each floor?

T: _____

I: _____

_____

N: _____

S: _____

_____

WORK SPACE

7. The fence around a square pool is 144 meters long. Each of the four sides of the fence are the same length. How long is each side?

T: _____

I: _____

_____

N: _____

S: _____

_____

WORK SPACE

8. Vanessa draws fifteen happy faces on her paper. Each happy face has two eyes. How many eyes did Vanessa draw on her paper?

T: _____

I: _____

_____

N: _____

S: _____

_____

WORK SPACE

9. There are eight schoolhouses in the city. Each schoolhouse has fourteen bells. How many bells do the schoolhouses have altogether?

T: _____

I: _____

_____

N: _____

S: _____

_____

WORK SPACE

10. Lilly's mother buys her twenty new T-shirts. She plans to wear two T-shirts a day at camp. How many days will Lilly be able to wear new T-shirts at camp?

T: _____

I: _____

_____

N: _____

S: _____

_____

WORK SPACE

11. Ms. Haga has twenty-four students in her class. She receives her order of forty-eight frog stickers on Tuesday. She wants to divide the stickers equally between the students in her class. How many frog stickers will each child receive?

T: _____

I: _____

_____

N: _____

S: _____

_____

WORK SPACE

12. Twenty-five cans of cranberry sauce are stacked at the end of the aisle at Mr. Mott's market. The cans are divided into 5 rows. How many cans are in each row?

T: _____

I: _____

_____

N: _____

S: _____

_____

WORK SPACE

13. Seven students go to a party. Each child receives a goody bag with thirteen sports pins in it. What is the total number of sports pins that all seven children receive?

WORK SPACE

T: _____

I: _____

_____

N: _____

S: _____

_____

14. Twelve black crows were sitting on the telephone wires. The crows split into 3 equal groups. How many crows are in each group?

WORK SPACE

T: _____

I: _____

_____

N: _____

S: _____

_____

15. Twelve monkeys are swinging in a tree. Each monkey eats nine bananas. How many bananas do the monkeys eat in all?

T: _____

I: _____

_____

N: _____

S: _____

_____

WORK SPACE

16. Brad has $120. He wants to give an equal amount of money to himself, Mark, Courtney, and Maureen. How much money will each person get?

T: _____

I: _____

_____

N: _____

S: _____

_____

WORK SPACE

17. Smiley School has sixty-four extra bottles of glue. The principal decides to separate the glue so that eight classes each get an equal number of bottles of glue. How many extra bottles of glue will each class receive?

T: _____

I: _____

_____

N: _____

S: _____

_____

WORK SPACE

18. Four friends each save $44 for a field trip. How much money do the girls save altogether?

T: _____

I: _____

_____

N: _____

S: _____

_____

WORK SPACE

19. Tom turned on two lamps. Each lamp uses three 75-watt bulbs. How many bulbs altogether were in Tom's lamps?

T: _____

I: _____

_____

N: _____

S: _____

_____

20. There are three elevators in the lobby of the building. Fifteen people want to go to the eighteenth floor. How many riders will travel in each elevator if the people are equally divided?

T: _____

I: _____

_____

N: _____

S: _____

_____

Final Mixed Review

Use TINS to solve these problems. Remember to circle key words and draw pictures.

1. Maggie bought a brand new bicycle. Both wheels on her bike have a total of 24 spokes. How many spokes are on each wheel?

Thought: _____

Information: _____

_____

Number Sentence: _____

Solution Sentence: _____

_____

WORK SPACE

2. Mr. Martinez went on a field trip with third graders to the zoo. 204 students rode on the bus to the zoo. Twenty-eight students rode home with their parents and did not take the bus back to school. How many students return to the school with Mr. Martinez?

T: _____

I: _____

_____

N: _____

S: _____

WORK SPACE

3. On Thursday a busy restaurant sold a total of 1,044 sandwiches. If 987 sandwiches were sold after 12:30 p.m., how many sandwiches were sold on Thursday before 12:30 p.m.?

T: _____

I: _____

_____

N: _____

S: _____

_____

WORK SPACE

4. Lorna has 81 grapes to share with her friends. She plans to give nine friends each an equal number of grapes. How many grapes will each friend get?

T: _____

I: _____

_____

N: _____

S: _____

_____

WORK SPACE

5. Matt's chess set contains 2 kings, 2 queens, 4 bishops, 4 rooks, 4 knights, and 16 pawns. How many chess pieces are in Matt's set?

T: _____

I: _____

_____

N: _____

S: _____

_____

WORK SPACE

6. Johnny has 243 stamps in his collection. His dad gives him 32 new stamps for his birthday. Sam has 188 stamps in his collection. How many stamps does Johnny have in all?

T: _____

I: _____

_____

N: _____

S: _____

_____

WORK SPACE

7. Mr. Booth bakes 2,197 bagels on Sunday morning. He sells 1,987 bagels that Sunday. How many bagels does Mr. Booth have left?

T: _____

I: _____

_____

N: _____

S: _____

_____

8. The computer room at Baty Elementary has five large tables. Each table has five computers on it. Students go to computers for one hour a day. What is the total number of computers in the Baty Elementary computer room?

T: _____

I: _____

_____

N: _____

S: _____

9. Donna is about to write a 12-page report for history class. Each day for 3 days, Donna wants to write an equal number of pages. How many pages will Donna need to write each day?

T: _____

I: _____

_____

N: _____

S: _____

WORK SPACE

10. The school store has twenty-five boxes of school supplies. Each box contains three pencils. How many pencils are there in all the school supply boxes?

T: _____

I: _____

_____

N: _____

S: _____

WORK SPACE

11. Jerry's class is going camping. He takes nineteen granola bars for the campout. Nine granola bars were eaten on the first day. How many granola bars does Jerry have left?

T: _____

I: _____

_____

N: _____

S: _____

WORK SPACE

12. Martina and Louis are taking a ten-hour train ride. They sleep for the first six hours of the train ride. How much time do they have left on the train?

T: _____

I: _____

_____

N: _____

S: _____

WORK SPACE

13. John Carlo has $39. He loans Jennifer $21. How much money does John Carlo have left?

T: _____

I: _____

_____

N: _____

S: _____

WORK SPACE

14. The library has 22 books about cats and 44 books about dogs. The librarian buys 14 more books on dogs. How many books on the subject of dogs does the library have now?

T: _____

I: _____

_____

N: _____

S: _____

WORK SPACE

15. Teronia plants five rows of tulips in her garden. Each row has eight bulbs in it. What is the total number of tulips Teronia plants?

T: _____

I: _____

_____

N: _____

S: _____

WORK SPACE

16. Matthew studies 2 hours on Monday, 3 hours on Tuesday, and 3 hours on Wednesday. He spends 6 hours at baseball practice on Saturday. What is the total number of hours Matthew studies during the three days?

T: _____

I: _____

_____

N: _____

S: _____

WORK SPACE

17. A large hotel has 102 lights in the lobby. Seventy-eight of the light bulbs burn out. How many lights are still lit in the lobby?

WORK SPACE

T: _____

I: _____

_____

N: _____

S: _____

18. There are 550 parking spaces at the airport terminal. The spaces are separated into 50 rows. How many cars can park in each row?

WORK SPACE

T: _____

I: _____

_____

N: _____

S: _____

19. Helen has 2 staircases on the outside of her house. Each staircase has 9 steps. How many steps does Helen have on the outside of her house?

T: _____

I: _____

_____

N: _____

S: _____

WORK SPACE

20. Savannah has a box of notebook paper. It contains 100 sheets. If she uses 78 sheets, how many pieces of notebook paper remain in her box?

T: _____

I: _____

_____

N: _____

S: _____

WORK SPACE

21. Both Claudette and Quatina decide to collect buttons. The children want to equally divide 20 buttons between themselves. How many buttons will each girl receive for her button collection?

T: _____

I: _____

_____

N: _____

S: _____

WORK SPACE

---

22. There were twenty-six sailboats out on the lake. Each sailboat has four sails. The sailboats all sailed for three hours. What was the total number of sails on all twenty-six sailboats?

T: _____

I: _____

_____

N: _____

S: _____

WORK SPACE

23. There are 30 contestants at the local juggler contest. Each person has 3 minutes to juggle with 6 balls. How many minutes will it take for all the jugglers to perform?

T: _____

I: _____

_____

N: _____

S: _____

WORK SPACE

24. Howie has 36 flowers to plant in his front yard. He wants to plant 6 flowers in each row. How many rows of flowers will Howie plant?

T: _____

I: _____

_____

N: _____

S: _____

WORK SPACE

25. At the beginning of the school year Mr. Ogle spent $202.98 on art supplies, $250.07 on school supplies and $199.21 on prizes for his students. What was the total amount of money Mr. Ogle spent?

T: _____

I: _____

_____

N: _____

S: _____

WORK SPACE

26. Mr. Clark has been asked to send out 2,333 letters containing information about the school fund-raiser. He has already mailed 1,212 letters. How many letters does Mr. Clark still need to mail?

T: _____

I: _____

_____

N: _____

S: _____

WORK SPACE

27. Susan has eight baskets and sixty-four eggs. She wants to put an equal number of eggs in each basket. How many eggs will Susan put in each basket?

T: _____

I: _____

_____

N: _____

S: _____

WORK SPACE

---

28. Louisa buys nine packages of pens. Each package contains fourteen pens. How many pens does Louisa have in all?

T: _____

I: _____

_____

N: _____

S: _____

WORK SPACE

29. Jason swims at the pool two hours a day for fifteen days. What is the total number of hours Jason swims during fifteen days?

WORK SPACE

T: _____

I: _____

_____

N: _____

S: _____

30. A movie is 108 minutes long. It is shown on television in 3 equal parts. How long is each part?

WORK SPACE

T: _____

I: _____

_____

N: _____

S: _____

31. Lupe has forty-nine basketballs. She wants to store the basketballs in seven boxes in the gym. Lupe wants each box to hold an equal number of basketballs. How many basketballs will be in each box?

T: _____

I: _____

_____

N: _____

S: _____

WORK SPACE

---

32. Sandy baby-sits for her cousins for five hours on Friday, three hours on Saturday, and three hours on Sunday. How many hours did Sandy baby-sit on Saturday and Sunday?

T: _____

I: _____

_____

N: _____

S: _____

WORK SPACE

33. There are 34 birthday candles on Ms. Harris's birthday cake. She blows out 18 of the candles. How many candles are still lit?

T: _____

I: _____

_____

N: _____

S: _____

WORK SPACE

34. Abraham Lincoln was elected President of the United States in 1860. John Kennedy was elected to the same office in 1960, a century later. How many years separates their elections?

T: _____

I: _____

_____

N: _____

S: _____

WORK SPACE

35. Lindsey has a fifty-dollar bill. She spends $17 at the grocery store. How much change does Lindsey receive back?

T: _____

I: _____

_____

N: _____

S: _____

WORK SPACE

36. There are 18 plants in Will's greenhouse. When the weather warms up, he will move 7 plants outside. How many plants will remain in the greenhouse?

T: _____

I: _____

_____

N: _____

S: _____

WORK SPACE

37. There are sixteen buckets filled with jump ropes at Baker Elementary School. Each bucket contains eleven jump ropes. How many jump ropes does Baker Elementary have?

T: _____

I: _____

_____

N: _____

S: _____

WORK SPACE

38. The Montopolis Recreation Center has three swimming pools. Forty-five children want to go swimming. The lifeguards want to divide the children equally between the three pools. How many children will swim in each pool?

T: _____

I: _____

_____

N: _____

S: _____

WORK SPACE

39. Salena has $150. Her brother has twice as much money. How much money does Salena's brother have?

T: _____

I: _____

_____

N: _____

S: _____

WORK SPACE

40. Julio has 78 books on his bookshelf. He buys 7 new books at the bookstore. How many books does Julio have now?

T: _____

I: _____

_____

N: _____

S: _____

WORK SPACE

41. Terri has fifteen gift certificates. She plans to share the certificates equally between Alex, David, and Elizabeth. How many gift certificates will each person receive?

T: _____

I: _____

_____

N: _____

S: _____

WORK SPACE

42. Lizzie is writing a story. She already has spent two hours writing each day for seven days. How many hours has Lizzie spent writing?

T: _____

I: _____

_____

N: _____

S: _____

WORK SPACE

Write Your Own

Write your own word problems. Then use TINS to solve them. Remember to draw pictures and circle key words. Happy problem writing!

---

1. Addition Word Problem: _____

_____

_____

_____

Thought: _____

Information: _____

_____

Number Sentence: _____

Solution Sentence: _____

_____

WORK SPACE

---

2. Subtraction Word Problem: _____

_____

_____

_____

T: _____

I: _____

_____

N: _____

S: _____

_____

WORK SPACE

3. Multiplication Word Problem: _____

_____

_____

_____

_____

T: _____

I: _____

_____

N: _____

S: _____

_____

4. Division Word Problem: _____

_____

_____

_____

_____

T: _____

I: _____

_____

N: _____

S: _____

_____

Reading Graphs and Charts to Solve Word Problems

Graphs and charts can be used to organize and report on facts. There are many different kinds of graphs. This section uses bar graphs and picture graphs. Each word problem in the following exercises uses either a graph or chart to present important information.

To solve a word problem using a graph (or a table), you will need to search the graph for important information. Then use TINS to answer the question.

After writing your THOUGHT (T), search the graph (or table) for the important INFORMATION (I). Then write your information as a NUMBER SENTENCE (N) and plug your answer into a SOLUTION SENTENCE (S).

Example: Bar Graph: Students were asked to sell tickets to the school play. The number of tickets sold by each student is shown in the graph. How many more tickets did Ann sell than Jane?

Thought: _____ — _____

Information: ___Ann 10, Jane 6___

Number Sentence: ___10 — 6 =___

Solution Sentence: ___Ann sold 4 more___

___tickets than Jane did.___

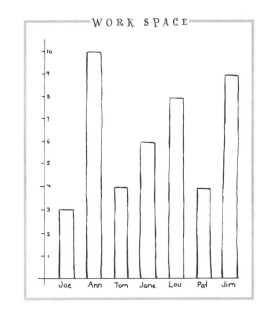

WORK SPACE

1. Picture graph: Blaney Elementary fourth graders took a survey to find out students' favorite sports.

How many more students prefer soccer than baseball?

Thought: _____

Information: _____

_____

Number Sentence: _____

Solution Sentence: _____

_____

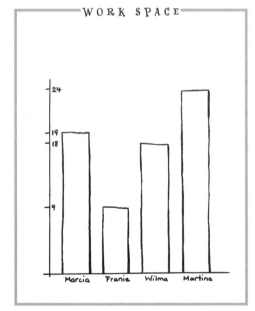

2. Bar Graph: Ms. Garcia and Ms. Ashcroft are keeping track of the number of miles students ran last week in gym class. Marcia ran 19 miles, Franie ran 9 miles, Wilma ran 18 miles, and Martina ran 24 miles. One side of the graph shows names and the other side shows numbers. How many miles did Marcia, Martina, and Wilma run altogether last week?

T: _____

I: _____

_____

N: _____

S: _____

_____

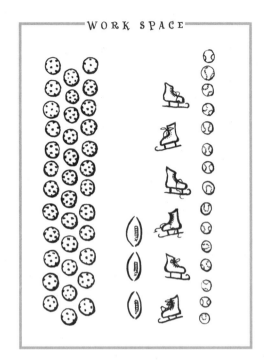

3. The play *Big* just finished touring four Texas cities. In San Antonio 456 people attended, in Austin 544 people attended, in Houston 786, and in Dallas 767 attended. What is the difference between the number of people who attended the play in Houston and the number of people who attended the play in Austin?

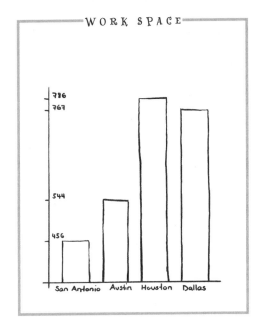

T: _____

I: _____

_____

N: _____

S: _____

_____

4. At Hello Café in San Francisco, a T-shirt costs $24, a mug costs $14, a hat costs $12, and socks cost $9. Abby purchased a T-shirt and hat at Hello Café. What is the total amount of money Abby spent?

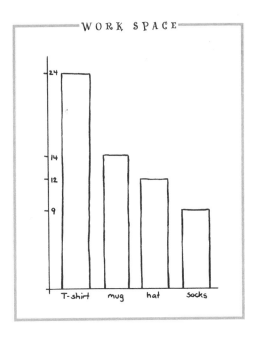

T: _____

I: _____

_____

N: _____

S: _____

_____

5. This picture graph shows that on the Hot Shot Soccer Team Lindsey scored 22 goals, Bianca 18, Miranda 14, Eli 16, and Samantha 10. How many more goals did Lindsey score then Eli?

T: _____

I: _____

_____

N: _____

S: _____

_____

WORK SPACE

Lindsay   Bianca   Miranda   Eli   Samantha

---

6. A picture graph shows that Matt sold 30 glasses of lemonade, Brett sold 25, and West sold 20. What is the total number of glasses of lemonade the three boys sold?

T: _____

I: _____

_____

N: _____

S: _____

_____

WORK SPACE

Matt   Brett   West

7. This bar graph that shows the number of books read by four classes at Poe Elementary during the month of September. Ms. Cren's class read 37 books, Mr. Bradshaw's read 43 books, Ms. Owen's 19 books, and Ms. Goodhue's 27 books. How many more books did Mr. Bradshaw's class read then Ms. Cren's class?

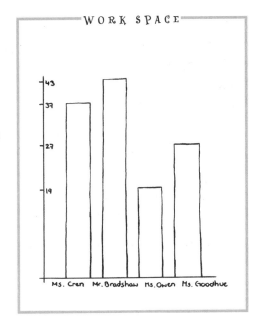

T: _____

I: _____

_____

N: _____

S: _____

_____

8. A veterinarian compared the weight of four animals staying in his clinic. A small dog weighed 43 pounds, a large dog weighed 84 pounds, a cat weighed 17 pounds, and a bird weighed 6 pounds. How much do the large dog and bird weigh altogether?

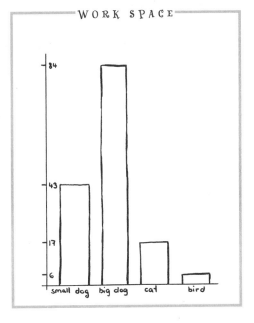

T: _____

I: _____

_____

N: _____

S: _____

_____

9. Three people went to lunch yesterday. Marcus spent $14, May spent $12, and John spent $16. How much money did May and John spend on lunch altogether?

T: _____

I: _____

_____

N: _____

S: _____

_____

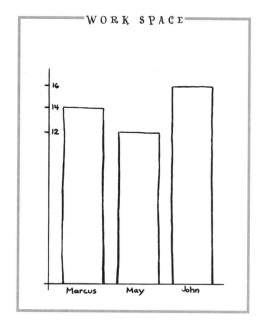

WORK SPACE

10. A picture graph shows 12 rainy days in June, 6 in July, and 24 in August. How many more days did it rain in August than in June?

T: _____

I: _____

_____

N: _____

S: _____

_____

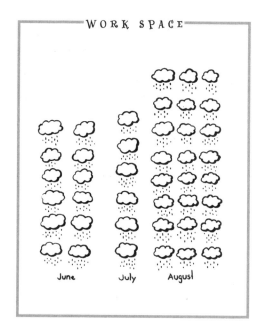

WORK SPACE

11. Mary's uncle was making cookies for the school bake sale. The pictograph shows he baked 16 raisin, 16 oatmeal, 24 peanut butter, and 32 vanilla cookies. How many oatmeal, raisin, and vanilla cookies did Mary's uncle bake altogether?

T: _____

I: _____

_____

N: _____

S: _____

_____

WORK SPACE

raisin   oatmeal   peanut butter   vanilla

12. Gerald took a survey to find out what color students wanted the halls painted at his school. White was picked by 123 students, ivory by 145, purple by 211, and grey by 244. What is the total number of votes the two most popular colors received?

T: _____

I: _____

_____

N: _____

S: _____

_____

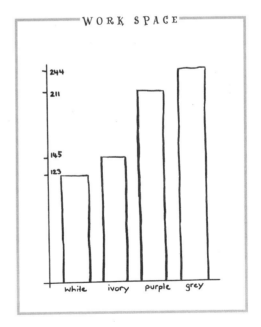

WORK SPACE

244

211

145

123

white   ivory   purple   grey

13. During a Geometric Walk to find different shapes around the school, Ms. Owenby's class recorded the following shapes: 17 spheres, 22 circles, 34 triangles, 19 squares, and 25 cylinders. How many more triangles than cylinders did Ms. Owenby's class see on their walk?

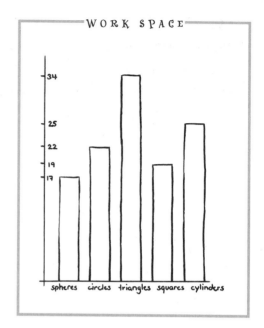

T: _____

I: _____

_____

N: _____

S: _____

_____

14. This bar graph shows Mr. Arrelano's students' favorite lunch items for the month of February: nine students chose peanut butter and jelly, eleven chose spaghetti, and eight chose lasagna. If twice as many people in Mr. Arrelano's class chose lasagna as their favorite item on the lunch menu, how many students in Mr. Arrelano's class voted for lasagna?

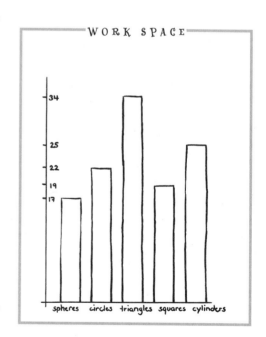

T: _____

I: _____

_____

N: _____

S: _____

_____

15. The students at St. Thomas School voted on their favorite type of music. A graph shows 44 prefer rock and roll, 36 like rap, 32 country, and 18 folk. How many more students preferred Rock and Roll than Country?

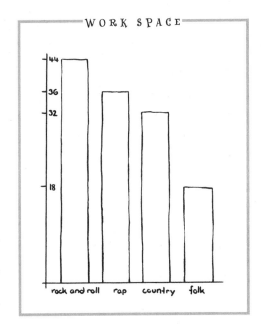

WORK SPACE

T: _____

I: _____

_____

N: _____

S: _____

_____

Write Your Own

Create your own bar graph and/or picture graph and write a word problem to go with it. Use the examples provided to make your own bar and picture graphs. Then create your own questions and record your results using the TINS method.

Remember a graph must include a title, a label for horizontal and vertical information, a grid, and available information.

---

1. Bar Graph: Record how many glasses of water you drink each day for one week.

Question: _____

_____

Thought: _____

Information: _____

_____

Number Sentence: _____

Solution Sentence: _____

_____

WORK SPACE

WRITE YOUR OWN   153

2. Picture Graph: On the last 6 days of Brenda's vacation, she picked apples in her grandfather's orchard. Later she wrote down the exact number of apples she picked.

Question: _____

_____

T: _____

I: _____

_____

N: _____

S: _____

_____

You can write the key words that you know in each operation sign.
Then cut out the signs and put them on your desk or in your math folder.